HERGÉ

THE ADVENTURES OF TINTIN

PRISONERS OF THE SUN

MAMMOTH

Translated by Leslie Lonsdale-Cooper
and Michael Turner

The TINTIN books are published in the following languages :

Afrikaans :		HUMAN & ROUSSEAU, Cape Town.
Arabic :		DAR AL-MAAREF, Cairo.
Basque :		MENSAJERO, Bilbao.
Brazilian :		DISTRIBUIDORA RECORD, Rio de Janeiro.
Breton :		CASTERMAN, Paris.
Catalan :		JUVENTUD, Barcelona.
Chinese :		EPOCH, Taipei.
Danish :		CARLSEN IF, Copenhagen.
Dutch :		CASTERMAN, Dronten.
English :	U.K. :	METHUEN CHILDREN'S BOOKS, London.
	Australia :	REED PUBLISHING AUSTRALIA, Melbourne.
	Canada :	REED PUBLISHING CANADA, Toronto.
	New Zealand :	REED PUBLISHING NEW ZEALAND, Auckland.
	Republic of South Africa :	STRUIK BOOK DISTRIBUTORS, Johannesburg.
	Singapore :	REED PUBLISHING ASIA, Singapore.
	Spain :	EDICIONES DEL PRADO, Madrid.
	Portugal :	EDICIONES DEL PRADO, Madrid.
	U.S.A.	LITTLE BROWN, Boston.
Esperanto :		CASTERMAN, Paris.
Finnish :		OTAVA, Helsinki.
French :		CASTERMAN, Paris-Tournai.
	Spain :	EDICIONES DEL PRADO, Madrid.
	Portugal :	EDICIONES DEL PRADO, Madrid.
Galician :		JUVENTUD, Barcelona.
German :		CARLSEN, Reinbek-Hamburg.
Greek :		ANGLO-HELLENIC, Athens.
Icelandic :		FJÖLVI, Reykjavik.
Indonesian :		INDIRA, Jakarta.
Iranian :		MODERN PRINTING HOUSE, Teheran.
Italian :		GANDUS, Genoa.
Japanese :		FUKUINKAN SHOTEN, Tokyo.
Korean :		UNIVERSAL PUBLICATIONS, Seoul.
Malay :		SHARIKAT UNITED, Pulau Pinang.
Norwegian :		SEMIC, Oslo.
Picard :		CASTERMAN, Paris.
Portuguese :		CENTRO DO LIVRO BRASILEIRO, Lisboa.
Provençal :		CASTERMAN, Paris.
Spanish :		JUVENTUD, Barcelona.
	Argentina :	JUVENTUD ARGENTINA, Buenos Aires.
	Mexico :	MARIN, Mexico.
	Peru :	DISTR. DE LIBROS DEL PACIFICO, Lima.
Serbo-Croatian :		DECJE NOVINE, Gornji Milanovac.
Swedish :		CARLSEN IF, Stockholm.
Welsh :		GWASG Y DREF WEN, Cardiff.

PRISONERS OF THE SUN

At Police Headquarters in Callao, Peru...

Haddock, a retired ship's captain, and Tintin, the reporter? Oh, yes, Interpol warned me they'd be coming. Send them in.

As I understand it, this is the situation: your friend Professor Calculus has been kidnapped, and you have good reason to believe he's aboard the cargo ship "Pachacamac"- due to arrive in Callao any day now. Am I right?[1]

Absolutely.

Well, gentlemen, as soon as the "Pachacamac" comes into port we will search the ship. If your friend really is aboard, then he will be restored to you immediately. Now, we can only...

Look down there; an Indian running away!... Someone was spying on us!

Surely you're mistaken...

No, no, I saw him quite clearly: an Indian, peering through the railings. He disappeared behind those bushes.

Bah! What does it matter? There was nothing confidential in what we said.

Why not forget the whole incident... and allow me to offer you a glass of pisco? It's our national drink. Come, here's to the safe return of your friend Calculus.

[1] See The Seven Crystal Balls

1

A few minutes later...

Our lucky day! Just think, we're going to see old Cuthbert again!... This is the happiest day of my life!... Hurrah for pisco! It's all right!... Everything's going to be all right!

Perk up, don't look so gloomy. We'll soon see Cuthbert again. Things are looking up!

Yes, things are looking up... But you know, it doesn't alter the fact that we're being watched.

Pooh, that doesn't matter! Enjoy yourself. Look around you: the Indians, the clothes, the colours, the llamas.

Kilikilikili!...There's a nice little llama...

Hoity toity! Aren't we grand!

You be careful, señor...

Be careful?... Why?...I'm not going to eat your precious llama, am I?...

You're a nice little llama, aren't you?... You don't mind old Captain Haddock, do you?

When llama is angry, señor, he always do that.

And what manners!

Ungrateful brute! Animals like that shouldn't be allowed!

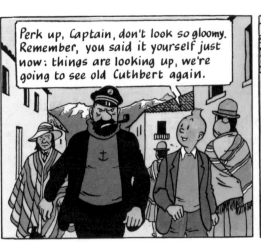

Perk up, Captain, don't look so gloomy. Remember, you said it yourself just now: things are looking up, we're going to see old Cuthbert again.

Hotel Cristobal Colon. Bueno...

The next morning...

RRRING

Hello... yes, Tintin speaking... Good morning, señor Chief Inspector... What?... The "Pachacamac" is in sight?... Fine!... Quay No. 24... We'll be there right away.

A few minutes later...

There's the Chief Inspector with his men, down on the quayside...

But... I must be seeing things... Look!

Thomson and Thompson! What are those nitwits doing here?

You asked about your friends... well, here they come.

What a coincidence!

Not at all. These gentlemen were sent out by the C.I.D. to help in the search for your friend.

Now for the "Pachacamac". Where is she?

Out there, to the left of that little tug with the red funnel ...

Ah, now I've got it ... There she is... it's her all right..."Pachacamac" ...Let's hope old Calculus is on board!

Thundering typhoons!

?

Blistering barnacles! The "Pachacamac" is running up the yellow flag and a yellow and blue pennant: infectious disease on board!

Goodness gracious! And we've got to go on board to search the ship.

It's out of the question till the port health authorities have cleared her...

There goes the doctor's launch now, heading for the "Pachacamac"...

Well... we can only wait until they've finished.

I say, Captain, just what is that stuff, guano?

Guano?... Er... How shall I put it?...

PLOP

Guano?... Well, there's a free sample!

So you think that's funny, eh?... A brand new hat!... Ha ha; very amusing.

PLOP

Captain... The "Pachacamac" is hoisting more flags!

4

Billions of blue bubonic barnacles! She'll be quarantined!

Are they celebrating the captain's birthday?

Putting a ship in quarantine, you landlubber, means keeping her in isolation for some time, to avoid risk of infection.

There's the launch coming back...

Well, doctor?

Two cases of yellow fever on board. I've ordered three weeks' quarantine.

You heard?...I'm terribly sorry about that...You'll just have to be patient.

Yes... obviously. Tell me, isn't that doctor an Indian?

A Quichua, as a matter of fact. Why?

Oh, no reason. I just wondered.

A little later...

Thundering typhoons! Three weeks...Three weeks without knowing whether Calculus is even aboard that blistering bathtub!

There's no question of waiting three weeks... We're going to find out tonight!

What do you mean, tonight?

Tonight I shall go aboard the "Pachacamac".

Tonight?...You?... What about the yellow fever, stupid?... Have you forgotten?

Captain, I'll bet anything you like that every man aboard the "Pachacamac" is as fit as you and me.

But thundering typhoons, the doctor definitely said...

The doctor is an Indian, Captain... a Quichua Indian... Doesn't that mean anything to you?...

Night has fallen...

Stop! We won't go any further... We might be seen.

Right... You're quite sure? I told you, there are sharks around here...

Nuts to the sharks! Anyway, they should be fast asleep at this hour, like everyone else!

Just as you like...

There... You know the drill, don't you: if I'm not back in a couple of hours, inform the police... Goodbye, Captain. And you be a good boy, Snowy.

Good luck, Tintin.

Thundering typhoons!... There's no stopping him!

Now comes the most difficult part...

¿Qué pasa, ahí abajo?...

¿Quien es?

Crumbs! Somebody else!

There's nothing for it... into this cabin, quick!

All's well, he didn't see me... He's going past...

¿Qué ha pasado, Chiquito?...

No es nada, debe de ser el gato...

Fine! They think it's a cat!

He's going back into his cabin... He's shut the door...Whew!...

ZZZZ
ZZZZ

!

Someone's in that bunk, I must get out of here!

Excuse me... A little further to the West!

There's only one person in the world who talks like that ...and that is...

Cuthbert Calculus!

Professor!...Professor! ...Wake up!...It's me, Tintin! Please, please wake up!

Thundering typhoons!... Those guano-gatherers are murdering Tintin!

Iconoclasts!...Pirates!... Just a few more strokes...

...and someone's going to get it in the neck!

?

Wooah! Wooah!

Blistering barnacles!

Wooah! Wooah!

And you shut up, you sea-lion, you!

Ah, there's Tintin.

Wooah!

Quick, climb aboard... Not hurt, are you?

No, not a scratch... But let's get out of here, fast!

Calculus is on board, Captain, I saw him. They're going to put him to death. They say he committed sacrilege by wearing an Inca bracelet.

Back to the shore! We must get rein-forcements!

You dash back to the town and alert the police. I'll stay here and keep watch.

No sleep for us tonight, Snowy.

I might've guessed!

All quiet. But after what's happened they're bound to make a move ... Yes, they're launching a boat. I hope the Captain gets help quickly...

A 'phone box, at last!

Hello... Yes...Police Headquarters ... What?...You want to talk to the señor Chief Inspector?... At this hour? Have you gone crazy?... The señor Chief Inspector is asleep!

Thundering typhoons, I know that! If he wasn't asleep you wouldn't have to wake him up!...Tell him it's very, very urgent!

You're breaking my heart!... Look, it may be urgent, but nobody wakes the señor Chief Inspector at four a.m.!

But you must wake him, I tell you, it's ... Hello... Hello... Hello...The blistering blundering bird-brain, he's hung up!

Meanwhile...

The boat's getting nearer... Come on, Snowy, but don't show yourself. We're going to take a closer look at them...

I've got an idea ...I'll ring up the Thompsons... Four, two, eight ...That's it...

RRRING RRRING RRRING

That sounds like the telephone.

To be precise: the telephone.

Great snakes... They're carrying Calculus ashore!

RRRRING

Are you going to answer it?

Me?... Certainly not ... how can I? I'm asleep!

Taking their time, the baboons!

RRRRING

You can't be asleep, you're talking to me!

You know very well that I talk in my sleep!

Blue blistering barnacles! I can't stand here all night!

Very well, I'll go. But next time, it's your turn!

RRRING RRRING

Hello?... Hello, Thomson?... And about time too!... This is Captain Haddock...

What?...Who?... Oh, yes, Captain Haddock... I... What?... Calculus?... Where?... Yes... Right... We'll come at once...

Half an hour later...

Nearly two hours since I left him...I hope he's all right.

There's our boat... I left Tintin here... But where is he?

Many hours later...

Here, boy... Have you met anyone along this road – a young European, with a white dog?

?

Yes... and I've met him before!

Tintin!.., You young rascal, you had me properly fooled!... Honestly, I'd never have recognised you... But why the disguise?

Come along...I'll explain.

Shortly after you left they brought Calculus ashore. They had accomplices waiting on the beach. They lifted Calculus on to a llama and led him away. I followed at a distance, making sure they didn't spot me ...

We came to Santa Clara, a small town. I hastily bought this cap and poncho in the market, so I was able to get close to them at the station and see them buy tickets to Jauga...

What did they do with Calculus?

Obviously they'd drugged him; he followed them like a sleep-walker ... Then the train left – without me, alas: I hadn't enough money for a ticket. After that I retraced my steps, hoping to find you...

Thundering typhoons!... The gangsters! Going off with Calculus!... But we'll catch the next train...

Of course! But unfortunately the train only runs every other day.

But why are you by yourself? Where are the police? Didn't you telephone them?

Still in bed...And the Thompsons are hot on your trail, somewhere...

Two days later...

Our seats are in the last coach, aren't they?

Sí, señor.

12

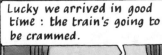
Lucky we arrived in good time: the train's going to be crammed.

No, no - it is impossible... You ask too much... I cannot...

It is _his_ order - and you know what happens to those who disobey him...

Half an hour later...

TOOOT

We're off... How odd: all that crowd of passengers, but not a soul has got into our compartment.

RESERVED

Have a good trip, señores!

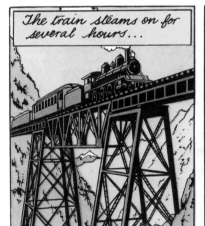
The train steams on for several hours...

Excuse me: I'll be back in a minute.

It's a funny thing... D'you know, we're absolutely alone in this carriage.

Strange... I say, while you were away I was looking at this travel guide. Imagine, on this line the train climbs to 15,865 feet over a distance of 108 miles... the highest railway in the world.

I'm not surprised: we've been going up steadily.

Hello, we're slowing down... I expect we're coming to a station.

!

Tintin!... Where is Tintin?

?

CRASH CRACK

Oh, look!... The coach has gone over the edge ... We just made it!

!

We can thank our lucky stars we got out of that, Snowy!

You're telling me!

First let's get dry... Then we must try to find the Captain ...

Come on Snowy, one last effort, you're nearly there.

Now, on our way. We must join up with the Cap- tain.

Still no sign ... Was he hurt when he jumped?

What has become of him?

16

Hooray!

Hooray!

Safe and sound! What an escape!

TOOOOT !

Hey, stop! ...Arrêtez! ... Whoa!

You were in the runaway coach? ...You were able to jump in time? ... How fortunate!

I am in charge at the next station... When the train arrived we found a coach missing...I was most upset: it is the first accident we have had on this line...

Accident? ...You mean attempted murder!

Attempted murder?...But that is impossible!

All the same, it's true. But don't let's waste time. We were going to Jauga... Will you take us there?

Some hours later, in Jauga

A short man, you say, with a little black beard, and glasses?...Yes, I think... Wait... He was accompanied by some Indians, wasn't he?

You mean he was a prisoner of the Indians. Our friend has been kidnapped.

Kidnapped by the Indians?...I... er... No, he wasn't the man you're looking for... The one I'm talking about seemed to be following the Indians quite willingly.

Naturally; he'd been drugged.

You think so?... That is not very likely... But now I come to think of it, the man...yes, the man I saw was tall, and fair...and clean-shaven.

But you told us yourself, just a moment ago...

I was mistaken, that's all...I am sorry I can be of no further assistance to you, gentlemen...The interview is closed!

Why that sudden change?...Curious ...He seemed anxious not to be involved. Is he afraid of the Indians?

Only one thing to do: split up and question some of the locals.

Right!...We'll meet outside the station in an hour.

You not look this way ... You tie up your shoelace ...

I know where your friend is prisoner...You buy guns and come tomorrow, at sunrise, to Bridge of the Inca...You understand?... Bridge of the Inca...You go now.

Fantastic! A guide, straight out of the blue!

What if it's a trap?

You listen to me, señor...

?

?

I see you go to help Indian boy ... You are good ... You are brave ...

Er...I... Who are you?

I speak wise words ... You not go in search of your friend, otherwise you meet many dangers.

How do you know?

I know, señor... You remember train that ran away...You have good luck that time... But you not always have good luck... You listen to me: you not go...

I can't abandon my friend - but thank you, anyway.

That is very foolish choice ... You still go, then take this... Very good, help you in danger ...

A little medal ... a talisman. What do you...

!

Next morning, at dawn ...

Blistering barnacles, why doesn't he show up, this guide of yours?

Pssst ... Psssst!

!

!

Quick, señores!... You come now!

Careful, be on your guard!

Why, it's the little orange-seller... the one I told you about.

So it was you...

Yes, I talk to you yesterday, from behind wall ...If Indians see me speak to you, they kill me at once... You come now...

You wait for me on other side of bridge... I come back quick.

Where's he off to?

I don't know. He told us to wait.

Thundering typhoons! Llamas!

To carry supplies, señores... Journey very long!

This is too much!... If you think I'm travelling around with this pair of perambulating fire-pumps, you're very much mistaken!

Llamas very gentle, señor. You not be afraid.

Afraid?... Me?... Afraid of these moth-eaten imitation camels?... I've only got to look them straight in the eye and they'll be eating out of my hand!

Like that... there!

YEEEEOW!

You miserable iconoclast!

You not hit him, señor.

21

When llama angry ...

Blistering barnacles, I know!... When llama angry, he always do that!

Come on, we've wasted enough time. ... Are we ready, er...? Look, we don't even know your name...

Zorrino, señor.

Now look, Zorrino: where is our friend ?... And why would none of the Indians tell us, though they all seemed to know what had happened to him?

He is prisoner in Temple of the Sun... But no one tell ... all afraid.

Afraid? Of whom?

Afraid of Inca, señor. Vengeance of Inca terrible when Indian tell white man what white man must not know.

The Inca?...The Temple of the Sun?... An Inca, in these days?... It's unbelievable.

White men not know, señor. Only you know.

Thanks to you, Zorrino; but aren't you afraid of the Inca, too?

Alone, I afraid: with you, I not afraid!

That evening...

There is chulpa, señor, old Inca tomb. We spend night there, go on again in morning.

I'll stand the first watch. At about midnight I'll wake you, and you can take over.

Right.

Good night, Captain. And don't forget to wake me in good time.

Don't worry, I will... Sleep well, both of you.

Good night, Zorrino.

Good night, señor Tintin.

Captain! What in the world...

Cut the cackle and get me out of this before I go crazy!

?

Billions of blistering... I ... I ...

Hooray! Got it!

This miserable reptile has spent the night waltzing along my spine!

A lizard!

Careful!

Hey, look! It's dropping to bits!

WOOAH! WOOAH!

WOOAH! WOOAH!

Now, Captain, what happened?

Well, it was getting on towards midnight and I was walking up and down to keep warm. Suddenly a shadow rose up in front of me. There wasn't time to move a muscle before ... Wham!... I felt a violent blow on the head... Next thing I knew, I was where you found me: tied up and gagged, with that lizard down my neck. What about Zorrino?

He's vanished, Captain, and so have the llamas, and our supplies. Much more serious, our guns have gone too!

Our guns?...The gangsters!... Bandits!...Filibusters!...Pirates!...

Thundering typhoons, what do we do now?

First of all, we must try to find Zorrino... Then tackle whoever's kidnapped him.

Help! he's fallen!...Ah, he's getting up...But they've caught him!

Here comes the last one...The others are out of sight...Now!

What's going on down there?

You tell, where is your friend?...Where Tintin?

No sé!

You know...You tell us; otherwise, you die.

Fiddle-de-dee to you...and abracadabra...and hocus pocus...

And fee-fi-fo-fum...And since you're so worried about my friend Tintin, take a look behind you!

? ?

All right, you thugs...Hands up!

Captain, will you disarm that Indian?...That's fine...Now if you'll untie Zorrino, I'll keep an eye on them...

Glad to see you, little'un.

All right?

Good!...That's disposed of them!

Señor!!

Hooray!

Come past me, Captain, while I cover you. You lot stay put!

Now then, get going down that path... fast! The first one who stops or comes back is a dead duck!...O.K.?...On your way...and take your pal with you!

I said fast!

Is no hurry ...

BANG

CRACK

I think they've got the idea! Now I'll rejoin the others.

You see, Zorrino, we didn't abandon you.

I know you save me. Where is Snowy?

We left him higher up: he couldn't climb down ... Look, there he is.

Hello, Snowy!

Wooah! Wooah!

?

Wooah! Wooah!

I've got a real bird's eye view!

Ooh! A condor!

!

Wooaaah!

Thundering typhoons!

Heavens! What can we do?... I daren't shoot...

Snowy! Oh, poor, poor Snowy!

WOOAH!

There... look... it's settled on a rock... Now or never!... Blistering barnacles, Tintin, be careful!

BANG

Hooray!

Quickly now! Ropes, and my scarf... I must go after Snowy...

You can't go up there!

You don't think I'd leave Snowy, Captain?... Injured, dying even...

Tintin, it's suicide, I tell you!

Snowy!... Snowy! ... No answer!

Snowy!... Snowy!

Not a sound!

Oh, it's you?... I say, these birds certainly know how to treat a guest!

!?

Whew! What a relief! He's safe...for the moment at least. Now he's got to come down...

Why couldn't you have answered, eh?...You're incorrigible!...Now, sit still!

This is it...down we go, gently now...

Oooh! I feel so giddy!...Why did I look?

Thundering typhoons!... Look, Zorrino! There! ...Another condor! Quick, my rifle!

BANG

WHIUUW

Missed, by thunder! ...And I can't fire again now: the condor has got him!

Oh, Tintin! Tintin! ...He'll be forced to let go!

It's all or nothing... I've no choice...

?

OOPS!

Blistering barnacles, what's going on?... He's hanging on to the condor's legs!...By thunder, what next?

Golly, a helicopter!

Quick!... Behind this rock!

Whew! That's better... It was a near thing... Quick, I must dig Zorrino out!

Where llamas?... And Captain?

I don't know, Zorrino ...Buried somewhere under the snow... We must find them.

Captain!... Captain!

Careful!... You not shout!

Crumbs! You're right! ...Will it...? No, nothing's moving now.

!

Wooah! Wooah!

The Captain!... He's found the Captain!

Come on! To work!... Where is he?

There!

No sign of life!... We must get him out... and quickly!

Poor Captain! Frozen stiff!

!

We ought to rub him briskly with alcohol... if we had some!...Ah, I'll bet he has a flask in his hip-pocket.

There ... I knew it!

Let's see now...

*?**

Whisky... fine!

!!!

?

Wait, Captain, not so fast!... Don't drink it all!

See, señores... Llamas not dead!

Good!...Hic...Fine!...I...I...I'll f-f-fetch them.

No, no, Captain! I'll go!

Y-you shut up, or I'll s-s-sneeze the mountain down! I...I...I s-s-started...hic...all this...hic...s-s-so I'll f-f-finish it!

But...

C-come here, you raggle-taggle ruminants!... H-here!

Y-you cushion-footed quadrupeds!...They run off as soon as I get near!...But I'll fix them!

C-come here you morons, and jump to it!...

As if he hasn't done enough damage already!

Look, there!...They must have been caught in an avalanche: only two of them left.

All the better: easier for us to deal with them! Come on!

I must be s-seeing things...d-down there!...The Indians who kidnapped Zorrino!

You know, Zorrino, the Captain's guardian angel has a full-time job!

Nothing broken, Captain?... That's lucky... Well, I reckon we've seen the last of those ruffians... Now, let's get back to the path...

Yes, yes...

I say, where's Snowy?... I don't remember seeing him around for quite a while... Snowy!... Snowy!...

Snowy!... Snowy!!... Where has he got to?

Good old Snowy! You've managed to dig out the Captain's cap.

We've found your cap; that's fine. But I'm afraid we've lost the llamas, and that means no more food, and no more ammunition...

No more ammunition?

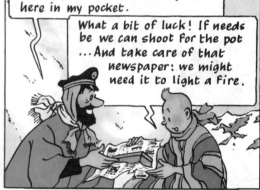

You needn't worry about that. Look: two boxes of cartridges, here in my pocket.

What a bit of luck! If needs be we can shoot for the pot ...And take care of that newspaper: we might need it to light a fire.

Many hours later...

You see, down there. Tomorrow we come into thick jungle.

Is the Temple of the Sun in the forest?

No, señor, temple still far away. We go through jungle. Then more mountains.

Blistering barnacles! Is there no end to it? I've had about enough of this little jaunt, I can tell you!

Stop!... Look, there's a cave!... Why don't we spend the night here?

Perhaps, but...

Don't worry. I'll look it over first.

CRACK
CRACK
CRACK

Tell me the truth. I can take it. I've been run over by a bus, haven't I?

Rubbish, Captain. It was a tapir.

When tapir in hurry, señor, tapir go straight on. He not worry for things in path. But tapir is not wicked, señor, not hard to tame him.

I'm glad to hear it. All the same, I'll use my gun to tame the next joker who comes along.

I can tell you one thing. Next time I need a nice, restful holiday, I'll know exactly where to come!

Ouch! These beastly mosquitoes!

Here is clearing. Good place to spend night.

Excellent idea...

Darkness falls...

Next day, at dawn...

ZZZZZ

ZZZZZ ZZZZZ
ZZZZZ

!

Mmmm...Snowy...Go away, Snowy... Leave me alone...

?

EEK!
HELP!

!

37

It's all right... It was only Zorrino breaking a dead branch.

You come, señores. I find canoe.

See...

Watch out, shipmates, this is going to be hot! ...Here they come! They've spotted us!

BANG

BANG

BANG

!

BANG

BANG

Loathsome brutes! Let me polish them off!

No, no! It's a waste of ammunition.

This beastly steaming jungle! ...Will it never end?

Tomorrow we leave forest, señor Captain.

The following evening...

We camp here tonight... Up there, in mountains, is Temple of the Sun.

Next morning ...

Off we go! ... I say, where did you find that rope?

For certain we need ropes ... I make them from jungle creepers.

What a torrent! We can't cross here : we'll have to try further up. The Temple of the Sun certainly has good defences !

Two days later ...

There's nothing for it, Captain : this is the only place ... You see that spike of rock over there ... We must try to lasso it with a rope.

Right !

Here goes !

O.K. I've fastened this end to a tree ... Now, who's first?

Hooray! Got it !

Zorrino, with señor Tintin's gun to test rope!

He's got guts, that boy !

Be careful, Zorrino !

Is O.K. !

Fine ... my turn next ...

Thundering typhoons! You need a cool head for this!

Blue blistering barnacles !

For heaven's sake, Captain, you'll fall... Leave your cap!

And buy another at the local hatter's, I suppose?

Whew! Done it!

Now it's my turn.

Oooh! Let's stop playing Tarzan!

Don't be silly, Snowy... We'll be all right...

Wooooah!

CRACK

Help!

All together again, Zorrino!

Tintin!... Oh, Tintin! ... Zorrino was so afraid. You not hurt?

No, not a scratch... I fell into the water and was sucked under... Then I don't know what happened... I was whirled around, and when I came to the surface I found myself in here.

It seems incredible, but I think I've stumbled on an entrance to the Temple of the Sun... so ancient that even the Incas themselves have probably forgotten all about it... Anyway, we'll soon see.

Blistering barnacles! It'll be as dark as the belly of a whale in there!

I thought so too. But I had a look. The rock is covered with some sort of phosphorescence which gives a little light. Shall we go?

No noise, now! ... Careful! ... I've got a hunch we're nearly at the end of our journey.

Calculus, here we come!

Where's this leading us?

If we keep going we'll soon see...

Now we're in trouble... The passage is blocked... There's no way of getting through.

The roof-fall was probably caused by an earthquake: they're pretty frequent in South America... Anyway, we're sunk now... unless...

Wooah! Wooah!

I've found the emergency exit!

Snowy seems to be on to something... It looks as though there's a way through there. Hold these, Zorrino, I'm going to try...

Any good?

I hope so.

Sacrilege!... Seize them!

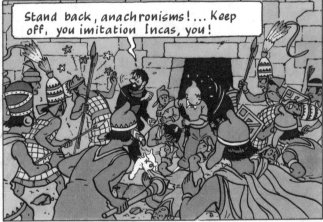

Stand back, anachronisms!... Keep off, you imitation Incas, you!

Tramps!... Zapotecs!... Pockmarks! ...Pithecanthropuses!... Bashi-bazouks!...Let me go, you savages!

Good! Now, hold them prisoner until we bring them before the Inca!

Sea-gherkins!... Ectoplasms!... Poltroons!... Politicians!... Dory-phores!... Terrorists!

Don't cry, Zorrino... We'll get out of this, you'll see...

Get out? Easier said than done... Poor Zorrino!

Hello, what's this at the bottom of my pocket..?

Ah, yes, the little coin that Indian gave me in Jauga ...I'd forgotten all about it.

"You still go, then take this...Very good, help you in danger!"

I wonder... perhaps it's some sort of talisman which protects whoever possess-es it... In that case it might save the life of one of us ...

Look, Zorrino, here's some-thing for you... Take good care of it: it might be very useful.

You come... The Inca waits.

Oho! He waits, does he?... Well, I've got a thing or two to say to his lordship!

Keep calm, Captain! Keep calm, I implore you ...

Great snakes! The Inca!

Look at that Indian on the left ...It's Chiquito, General Alcazar's music-hall partner ...The man I saw on the "Pachacamac."

Strangers, it is our command that you re-veal by what trickery you have entered the Temple of the Sun.

I...er... Noble Prince of the Sun, we found the entrance quite by chance, when I was swept into a waterfall.

Be that as it may, our laws decree but one penalty. Those who violate the sacred temple where we pre-serve the ancient rites of the Sun God shall be put to death!

Be put to death!... D'you really think we'll let ourselves be massacred, just like that, you tin-hatted tyrant?!

Captain, please! Keep quiet!

Noble Prince of the Sun, I crave your indulgence. Let me tell you our story. We have never sought to commit sacrilege. We were simply looking for our friend, Professor Calculus...

Your friend dared to wear the sacred bracelet of Rascar Capac. Your friend will likewise be put to death!

Blistering barnacles, you've no right to kill him! No more than you have a right to kill us, thundering typhoons! It's murder, pure and simple!

But it is not we who will put you to death. It is the Sun himself, for his rays will set alight the pyre for which you are destined.

As for this young Indian who guided these strangers and thus betrayed his race, he will suffer the penalty reserved for traitors!... He will be sacrificed immediately on the altar of the Sun God!

Billions of blue blistering barnacles! The first one who touches a hair of that boy's head is a dead duck!

Grrr!...

Great snakes! I just remembered! Your medal, Zorrino! ...Show them!

?

Where did you steal that, little viper?

I not steal, noble Prince of the Sun, I not steal! ...He give me this medal! ...I not steal!

And you, foreign dog, where did you get it? Like others of your kind, you robbed the tombs of our ancestors, no doubt!

Noble Prince of the Sun, I beg leave to speak...

!

It is I, noble Prince of the Sun, who gave the sacred token to this young stranger.

You, Huascar?... A high priest of the Sun God, you committed sacrilege and gave this talisman to an enemy of our race?

He is not an enemy of our race, noble Prince of the Sun... with my own eyes I saw him go alone to the defence of this boy, when the child was being ill-treated by two of those vile foreigners whom we hate. For that reason, knowing that he would face other great dangers, I gave him the token. Did I do wrong, illustrious Prince?

No, Huascar, you did nobly. But your action will save only this young Indian, for his life is protected by the talisman.

It will not save the young stranger; by his generosity he forfeited his only safeguard. Our laws are explicit: he will be put to death with his companion.

Nevertheless, I will grant them one favour...

I knew it: his bark's worse than his bite!

It is this: Within the next thirty days, they must die. But they may choose the day and the hour when the rays of the sacred Sun will light their pyre.

...They must give their answer tomorrow. As for this young Indian, he will be separated from his companions and his life will be spared. But he will stay within our temple until he dies, lest our secrets be divulged.

Now, let the strangers be taken away and kept in close confinement until tomorrow. The Prince of the Sun has spoken!

Well, we're in up to our necks, this time!

I know... But I'm glad Zorrino's safe, anyway.

Bunch of savages!... What I need is a pipe to calm my nerves... Where is it?... Ah, got it... Hello, what's this?

Oh yes, I remember... the newspaper we saved to light a fire.

Well, we shan't be needing that now... There'll be a fire all right...

But, thundering typhoons, we shan't be lighting it!

How do we get out of here?

These bars, perhaps? ... No, they're firmly fixed...

Anyway, even if we did manage to shift them, this window overlooks a precipice.

Blistering barnacles! I've lost my matches!

Give me your pipe, Captain. I've got a little magnifying-glass.

A magnifying-glass?

Why, it's alight!

Yes, look... that's done it.

Easy as winking!... It's amazing!... Marvellous!

Marvellous, yes... And that's precisely how the Incas will light up their bonfire when they set about roasting us.

...Unless they use parabolic mirrors, like Archimedes when he burnt the Roman ships beseiging Syracuse.

My pipe!

My pipe!...My poor pipe!... Blistering barnacles, it's broken!

Hello, Snowy, what are you doing? Where did you find that paper?

Meanwhile, in Europe...

We've searched South America from top to bottom, sir, without result. We lost all trace of Tintin, the Captain and the Professor.

To be precise: we got lost.

We have now decided to undertake a fresh search using entirely new methods. It's the only way; otherwise we have absolutely no hope.

To be precise: we're absolutely hopeless.

I see ... And what are your new methods?

You must allow us to preserve absolute secrecy, sir... "Dumb's the word": that's our motto.

Dowsing, my dear Thompson, like Professor Calculus; that'll put us on their track.

Captain! Captain! We're saved!

Saved?... What do you mean?

Well, you see, I... No... I don't think I'd better tell you. I could be wrong, and I don't want to raise any false hopes...

But I...

Listen, Captain: you must trust me, and promise to do exactly as I say, without hesitation. You'll understand later on.

Well, yes, but...

Yes?... Good: that's a promise!... Now we must be patient... While we're waiting I'll mend your pipe...

Meanwhile...

Why, they aren't here!... How peculiar! The pendulum definitely indicates that they are somewhere high up.

The next morning...

Well, strangers; have you decided upon the day and the hour of your death?

Yes, noble Prince of the Sun... I wish... we wish to die in... er... eighteen days' time, at 11.0 o'clock... It is my friend's birth-day, and...

?

Tintin, you're crazy! ... You know it isn't...

Quiet, Captain!... You promised to trust me.

So be it!... In eighteen days, at the hour you have chosen, you shall atone for your crime. Guards, take them away. Let them be well treated, and let their least wish be granted!

A few minutes later...

Here, señores. You stay in royal apartment now...

Now, will you kindly explain what this is all about?

Not yet, Captain, not yet. But you can be sure of one thing: there's nothing to worry about!

Nothing to worry about!...Not a sausage!... We're only going to be roasted alive in eighteen days' time: apart from that, there's nothing to worry about!...To be precise, as Thompson and Thomson would say, nothing at all!

Time goes by...

Only seven more days...Thundering typhoons, we're in a real jam!

Next morning...

How can we get out?...Who can help us?...Zorrino, perhaps...

The next day...

It's a fine time for gymnastics! Blistering barnacles, here we are with five days to live, and you do morning exercises!

Why not, Captain? One must keep fit.

Keep fit! Keep fit!...Thundering typhoons! I don't need exercises to keep me fit!...I'll show you just how fit I am: at my age, too!

Watch this: a standing jump, feet together, clean over the table.

HUP!

My, my!

So you think that's funny, eh?

54

Only four days left...

No one's going to say that I allowed myself to be roasted like a turkey on a spit!...We must do something!

You know quite well that's impossible.

Only three days...

What can we do, thundering typhoons!?

Round and round...he's making me giddy!

Only two days to go...

How can you lie there, just lounging around! ...Billions of blistering barnacles! We must do something!

Trust me, Captain. In two days' time we'll be free.

One day left...

It's all over!... Nothing to hope for! I never knew things could look so black!

At that moment...

According to the pendulum they're very low...

Next morning...

Only a few hours to live, and all you can do is read that bit of newspaper for the hundredth time!

"...The Swiss expedition is on its way to the Western Cordillera in the Andes. It will..." The rest is torn away.

Blistering barnacles! If it weren't for these confounded bars I'd soon be out of here!

CRACK
BANG
BOOM
?

!?*!

We're free!... Tintin, we're free!...Come on quickly, hurry! ...Out!

Don't do it, Captain! You'll break your neck!

Aha! We are just in time!

Thundering typhoons! ...Too late!

I wonder what that music is?

If you call it that!

BOOM BOOM

BOOM BOOM BOOM BOOM

Pacharurac-Pachacamac Viracocha

Cayhinapac Churasunqui Camasunqui

Captain, there's Professor Calculus! ...Old Cuthbert, after our long search!... Here he comes. They're going to tie him up beside us.

Why, Captain!...What a delightful surprise!... How are you?

Very well, thanks, as you can see!

And you too, my dear Tintin!...I'm so pleased to see you again!... But tell me, what is all this performance? ...Where are we?

With the Incas...

Ah, the cinema!...Good, I quite understand...Some historical drama, no doubt...Those people there are dressed like... like Aztecs, I think...Or rather, I should say, Incas.

Incas, exactly. Now you've got it.

Yes, their make-up is perfect... And look at those dancers; so natural: who'd believe they are acting.

Supposing I'm wrong...

Noble Prince, it is the hour of sacrifice!

Meanwhile...

According to the pendulum, they should be in a very hot spot...

Let the sacrifice begin! ... Let the High Priest of the Sun advance to the pyre!

What's that thing he's got there?

That's the burning glass to set our bonfire alight.

No?

Let me go! You mustn't kill them!

O Pachacamac, blessed lord of the day, maker of earth, god of life, strike now with thine avenging rays!

Stay, Huascar! ...The Sun God will not hear your prayers!

?

?

Grrr!

O magnificent Sun, if it is thy will that we should live, give us now a sign!

Silence, foreign dog! How dare you call upon the Sun?

O God of the Sun, sublime Pachacamac, display thy power, I implore thee! ... If this sacrifice is not thy will, hide thy shining face from us!

Poor Tintin, he's gone off his head!

Not at all: your hat is very chic.

I thank thee, supreme majesty! My prayer is answered; the darkness moves across thy face.

But... blistering barnacles, he's right! ... Have I gone crazy too? ... It's magic!

!

What superb acting! They look genuinely terrified...And what an idea to wait for a real eclipse! Brilliant!

An eclipse!... An eclipse!! ... An eclipse !!! ...

Don't be afraid. An eclipse, it is, that's all Captain.

Wow-ow -woo- ow!

Mercy, O stranger, I implore you!...Make the Sun show his light again, and I will grant whatever you desire!

So be it, noble Inca. I accept your word... Have no fear: I will entreat the Sun to reappear.

Wow-ow-oowow!

O Sun, lord of the day, show mercy, I pray thee... Pity thy children and show thy light once more!

Wow-ow-wow!

By Pachacamac! The Sun obeys him! ...Quickly! Set them free!

You see now, Captain? The newspaper!

It's ...it's miraculous !

Supreme lord of the day, we thank thee for thy mercy!

"I've got the sun in the morning..." ♫ ♫

A little more dignity, Captain, as befits those who command the sun!

Meanwhile ...

Still nothing, yet the pendulum shows they are getting bumped about !

Next day...

I keep my word, noble strangers: you are free... My men will escort you to the foot of the mountains.

Thank you, noble Prince, but I have one further request...

In my country there are seven learned men who are still, I imagine, enduring terrible torture because of you. By some means you have them in your power. I beg you to end their suffering.

These men came here like hyenas, violating our tombs and plundering our sacred treasures. They deserve the punishment I have meted out.

No, they did not come to plunder, noble Prince of the Sun. Their sole purpose was to make known to the world your ancient customs and the splendours of your civilisation.

So be it. I think you speak truth... It shall be done. Follow me, noble strangers, and in your presence I will put an end to their torment.

Each of these images represents one of the men for whom you plead. Here in this chamber, by our hidden powers, we have tortured them. It is here that we will release them from their punishment.

Witchcraft!... I can't believe it!... But the crystal balls: what were they for?

The crystal balls contained a mystic liquid, obtained from coca, which plunged the victims into a deep sleep. The High Priest cast his spell over them...and could use them as he willed.

Now I see it all!...That explains the seven crystal balls, and the extraordinary illness of the explorers. Each time the High Priest tortured the wax images the explorers suffered those terrible agonies.

Destroy the images, Huaco!

At that moment, in Europe...

What am I doing here?

What's happened? ...How did I get into hospital? ...

Where are we, Carling?

That's what I'm wondering, Sanders.

You here, Reedbuck?

Clarkson!... What in the world...

How did I get here?

See! The treasure of the Incas, for which the Spanish conquerors searched in vain for so long!

It seems unlikely, but there is gold around here somewhere. My pendulum never lies.

Several days later...

Now, señores, we leave you here. You take the train and return to your own country... Adios, señores, and may the sun shine upon you!

Just a minute... Don't go...

Will you hang on to my gun for a second?

Of course, but what's up?

Water?... The Captain drinking water?... I'd never have believed the day would come!

Rum?... You think so?

?

?

I've nothing against you personally, but that pays a very old debt!

THE END